Roar, roar, roar...

This angry Tyrannosaurus rex is hunting for food!

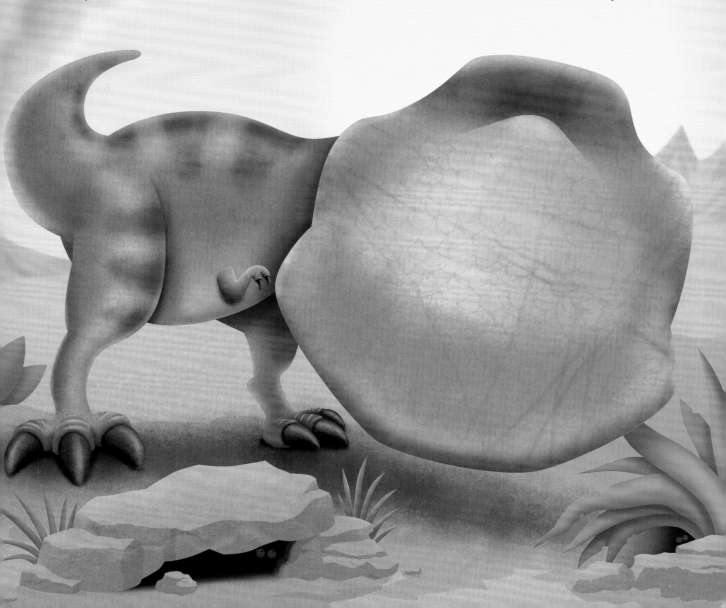

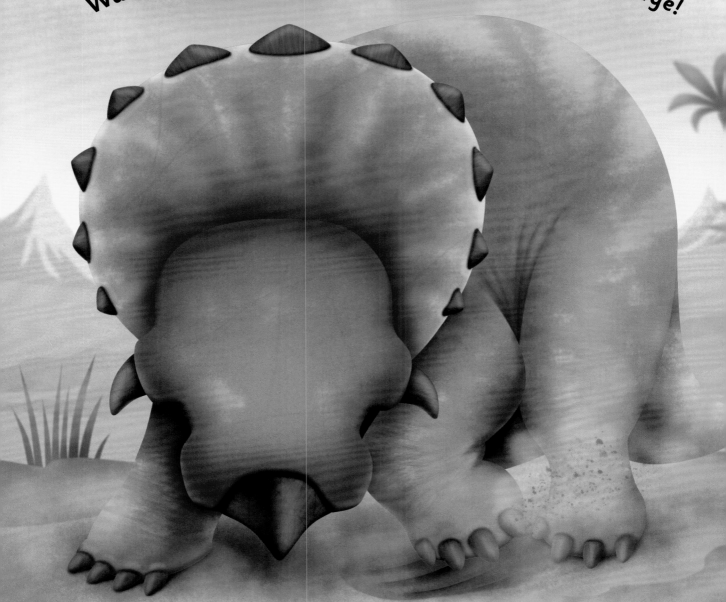

Snort, stamp, snort...

Watch out! This Triceratops is getting ready to charge!

Thud, thud, thud...

This giant Stegosaurus is not very clever!

Slash, slash, slash...
The sickle-clawed Deinonychus
hunts in a pack.

Bang, bang, bang...
Pachycephalosaurus uses its thick skull
as a battering ram!

Munch, munch, munch...
The enormous Diplodocus
has a huge appetite!

Swish, swish, swish...
Watch out for the Ankylosaurus'
clubbed tail!